SKIPPING RHYMES

SELECTED BY PIE CORBETT
ILLUSTRATED BY COLIN & MOIRA MACLEAN

Kingfisher Books

Kingfisher Books, Grisewood & Dempsey Ltd,
Elsley House, 24–30 Great Titchfield Street, London W1P 7AD

First published in 1993 by Kingfisher Books
2 4 6 8 10 9 7 5 3 1
This selection copyright © Pie Corbett 1993
Illustrations copyright © Colin and Moira Maclean 1989, 1993

Some of the material in this edition was previously published by Kingfisher Books
in *The Kingfisher Playtime Treasury*, selection copyright © Pie Corbett 1989

BRITISH LIBRARY CATALOGUING-IN-PUBLICATION DATA
A catalogue record for this book is available from the British Library

ISBN 1 85697 133 3

Phototypeset by Southern Positives and Negatives (SPAN), Lingfield, Surrey
Printed and bound in Spain

CONTENTS

Hippety hop to the candy shop 4
Two, four, six, eight 4
Under the stars 5
Roly poly 5
Andy Pandy 6
Jelly in the bowl 6
Akabacka soda cracker 6
Blue bells, cockle shells 7
Salt, mustard, vinegar, pepper 8
Mabel, Mabel 9
Mother made a chocolate cake 9
I like coffee 10
I'm a girl guide 11

Underneath the apple tree 12
Lemon pie, apple tart 13
I went to the animal fair 15
Bumper car, bumper car 16
Teddy bear, teddy bear 17
Not last night 19
Early in the morning 20
Peel a banana upside-down 21
Bread and butter 21
Charlie Chaplin went to France 22
Cinderella, dressed in yella 22
All in together 23
Index of first lines 24

Some easy rhymes to start you off . . .

Hippety hop to the candy shop
To buy a stick of candy.
One for you,
One for me,
One for sister Sandy.

Mark two lines on the ground with skipping ropes. Hop from one to the other. Widen the gap between the two ropes little by little.

Two, four, six, eight,
Johnny saw a rattlesnake
Eating cake by a lake,
Two, four, six, eight.

Lay the skipping rope on the ground like a snake. Try to walk along its back.

Under the stars,
Over the moon.

The rope is held by two players – the enders – who move it up and down as they chant the rhyme. On UNDER the other players run under the rope; on OVER they jump over it.

Roly poly,
Barley sugar.

Without a rope practise skipping from one leg to the other. Sing as you skip.

Rhymes to skip to on your own . . .

Andy Pandy,
Sugary Candy,
French Almond,
Nuts!

*Start skipping slowly and
speed up gradually.*

Jelly in the bowl,
Jelly in the bowl.
Wiggy waggy, wiggy waggy,
Jelly in the bowl.

*Skip in time to the rhyme and on
WIGGY WAGGY wiggle your hips
like jelly.*

Akabacka soda cracker,
Does your father chew tobacca?
Yes-No-Maybe so,
Yes-No-Maybe so . . .

*Keep repeating the last line until you
make a mistake. Whichever word you
land on will give you the answer!*

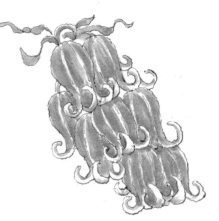

Blue bells, cockle shells,
Eavy, Ivy, O-ver,
The boys are in the clover.
Mother's in the kitchen,
Doing all the stitchin'.
How many stitches can she do?
1, 2, 3, 4, 5, . . .

Continue the numbers until you trip up.
Then you'll know how many stitches
Mother can do.

Salt, mustard, vinegar, pepper,
French almond rock.
Bread and butter for our supper,
That's all Mother's got.
Eggs and bacon, salted heron,
Pease pudding in a pot,
Pickled onions, apple pudding,
We will eat the lot.

When you get to PEPPER, try doing the bumps. This means turning the rope very fast to go under you twice in one skip.

Mabel, Mabel, set the table.
 Don't forget the
 Salt, mustard,
 Vinegar, pepper.

Try doing the bumps on SALT,
MUSTARD, VINEGAR and PEPPER.

Mother made a chocolate cake.
How many eggs did she break?
1, 2, 3, . . .

To make this a little more difficult, try doing
the bumps to see how many eggs were broken.

I like coffee,
I like tea,
I like *Jamie*
In with me.

I hate coffee,
I hate tea,
I don't want *Jamie*
In with me.

*In this rhyme choose a friend to skip
in with you. On the second verse your
friend skips out.*

Rhymes for skipping with three or more...

I'm a girl guide, dressed in blue,
Here are the actions I must do:
Salute to the captain,
Bow to the Queen,
Turn right round
And count sixteen.
1, 2, 3, 4, 5, . . . 16.

Two people turn the rope while the skipper mimes
the actions of the rhyme, counting up to 16 at the end.

Two people swing the rope and everyone takes it in turns to find out their future.

Underneath the apple tree
A boy said to me –
Kiss me, cuddle me,
Who should it be?
A-B-C-D . . .

Will you get married?
Yes, No, Yes, No, . . .

What will he marry you in?
Silk, satin, cotton, rags, . . .

How will you go to your wedding?
Coach, carriage, wheelbarrow, car, . . .

How many children?
1, 2, 3, 4, 5, . . .

The skipper skips until she trips on a letter. Then the others choose a boy's name beginning with that letter. The skipper skips on to discover if they will marry. If the answer is YES, she carries on to find out what she will wear, and so on.

Skip this game to find out who you will marry!

Lemon pie, apple tart,
Tell me the name of your sweetheart.
A-B-C-D-E-F . . .

Felix is your love,
White doves up above,
Sitting on his knee,
Under the apple tree,
Kissing 1, 2, 3, 4, . . .

Two people turn the rope while the skipper skips until she trips. Then her friends choose someone she knows whose name begins with that letter – for example, F for Felix. She skips again to find out how many kisses she gets!

13

I went to the animal fair,
The birds and beasts were there.
By the light of the moon, the gay baboon
Was combing his golden hair.
The monkey fell out of his bunk,
Slid down the elephant's trunk;
The elephant sneezed
And fell on his knees,
And what became of the monkey,
Monkey, monkey,
Monkey, monk!

*A chant for group skipping. Two players
turn the rope and everyone skips in. If
someone makes a mistake, he is out. Skip
on until only one person is left in.*

Two players swing the rope and everyone takes it in turns to skip.

Bumper car, bumper car,
Number 48,
Whizzed round the cooooorner . . .

The skipper leaves the rope, runs right round one end and runs in again.

. . . And slammed on the brakes.

The skipper traps the rope between his legs and then starts skipping again.

Brakes didn't work,
Slid down the hill,
Landed in the duck pond
And then stood still.
How many fishes can you see?
1, 2, 3, 4, 5, . . .

The skipper with the highest number of fishes before he trips wins the game.

Teddy bear, teddy bear,
Turn around.
Teddy bear, teddy bear,
Touch the ground.

Teddy bear, teddy bear,
Hands on head.
Teddy bear, teddy bear,
Go to bed.

Teddy bear, teddy bear,
Jump the stairs.
Teddy bear, teddy bear,
Say your prayers.

Teddy bear, teddy bear,
Turn out the light.
Teddy bear, teddy bear,
Spell goodnight.

G-O-O-D  N-I-G-H-T

*Two players swing the rope and everyone takes it in turns to skip
in and do the actions. At the end, the skipper spells out
GOODNIGHT while the enders turn the rope faster and faster.*

N ot last night
But the night before,
Twenty-four robbers
Came knocking at my door.
Went downstairs to let them in
And this is what I saw:

Spanish lady, Spanish lady,
Do high kicks.

Spanish lady, Spanish lady,
Take a bow.

Spanish lady, Spanish lady,
That's all for now.

Two players swing the rope. Everyone takes it in turns to skip in, in pairs, and do the actions.

Early in the morning at half-past eight,
I heard the postman knocking at the gate.
Up jumps *Lucy* to open the door,
How many letters fell on the floor?
1, 2, 3, 4, 5, . . .

Who from?
A-B-C-D-E . . .

Two people turn the rope. After
*JUMPS, they name a friend,
who skips in. She carries on
skipping until she stumbles on a
number, which tells her how
many letters she got. She skips
on to find out who sent them.*

Peel a banana upside-down,
Peel an orange round and round.
If you can jump to twenty-four,
You can have a go once more.
1, 2, 3, 4, . . .

*Two players swing the rope while the
others take it in turns to see who
can keep skipping till 24.*

Bread and butter, sugar and spice,
How many *boys* think I'm nice?
1, 2, 3, 4, . . .

*Keep skipping until you make a
mistake. The number you trip up on tells
you how many boys or girls like you!*

Charlie Chaplin went to France
To teach the ladies how to dance:
   Heel, toe, round you go.
   Salute to the captain,
   Bow to the Queen,
   Turn your back
   On the dirty submarine.

*While two players turn the rope, skip in and
mime the actions. On HEEL jump and put your
heel down, on TOE jump and point your toe.
On SALUTE pretend to salute, then jump and
BOW. On the last two lines run out of the rope
and right round to start again.*

Cinderella, dressed in yella,
Went upstairs and kissed her fella.
How many kisses did she get?
1, 2, 3, . . .

*Two players turn the rope. The number the
skipper trips on tells her how many kisses
she got!*

All in together,
No matter what the weather.
I spy Jack,
Peeping through a crack.
One, two, three,
Busy, busy, bee;
Nineteen, twenty,
Leave the rope empty.

January, February, March, April,
May, June, July, August,
September, October,
November, December.

*A chant for group skipping. Two players
turn the rope. Everyone else skips, jumping
out on the month of their birthday.*

23

INDEX OF FIRST LINES

Akabacka soda cracker	6	Jelly in the bowl	6
All in together	23	Lemon pie, apple tart	13
Andy Pandy	6	Mabel, Mabel, set the table	9
Blue bells, cockle shells	7	Mother made a chocolate cake	9
Bread and butter, sugar and spice	21	Not last night	19
Bumper car, bumper car	16	Peel a banana upside-down	21
Charlie Chaplin went to France	22	Roly poly	5
Cinderella, dressed in yella	22	Salt, mustard, vinegar, pepper	8
Early in the morning at half past eight	20	Teddy bear, teddy bear	17
Hippety hop to the candy shop	4	Two, four, six, eight	4
I like coffee	10	Underneath the apple tree	12
I'm a girl guide, dressed in blue	11	Under the stars	5
I went to the animal fair	15